# FOCUS ON ELEMENTARY

# CHEMISTRY

## Laboratory Notebook
### 3rd Edition

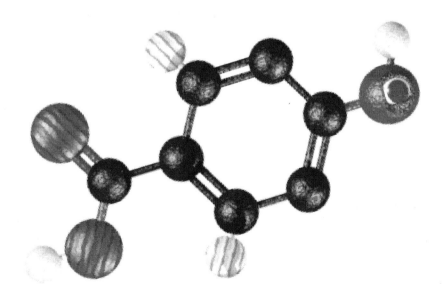

# Rebecca W. Keller, PhD

# Real Science-4-Kids

Illustrations: Janet Moneymaker

Focus On Elementary Chemistry Laboratory Notebook—3rd Edition
ISBN 978-1-941181-37-9

Published by Gravitas Publications Inc.
www.gravitaspublications.com
www.realscience4kids.com

## A Note From the Author

Hi!

In this curriculum you are going to learn the first step of the scientific method:

### Making good observations!

In the science of chemistry, making good observations is very important.

Each experiment in this notebook has several different sections. In the section called *Observe It*, you will be asked to make observations. In the *Think About It* section you will answer questions. There is a section called *What Did You Discover?* where you will write down or draw what you observed from the experiment. And finally, in the section *Why?* you will learn about the reasons why you may have observed certain things during your experiment.

These experiments will help you learn the first step of the scientific method and..... they're lots of fun!

Enjoy!

*Rebecca W. Keller, PhD*

# Contents

# Experiment 1

## Chemistry Every Day

People have always used chemistry in their lives, but before it became a science, people did not know how chemistry made things work. In this experiment you will explore how you use chemistry every day.

## I. Think About It

❶ Think about whether or not the things you do in a day involve any chemistry. Think about what you do, where you go, and what you eat.

❷ Make a list of some of the things you do in a day.

_____

_____

_____

_____

_____

_____

❸ Do any of these activities involve chemistry? Why or why not?

_____

_____

_____

_____

_____

## II. Observe It

Make a list of everything you do in one day. Start with the first thing you do in the morning and observe yourself throughout the day. Write down what you do, what you eat, how your food is prepared, where you go, and how you get there.

_____

_____

_____

_____

_____

_____

_____

_____

_____

_____

_____

_____

_____

_____

## III. What Did You Discover?

**❶** Do you use chemistry when you brush your teeth with toothpaste? Why or why not?

_____

_____

_____

**❷** Do you use chemistry when cooking food? Why or why not?

_____

_____

_____

**❸** Do you use chemistry when you eat food? Why or why not?

_____

_____

_____

**❹** Do you use chemistry when you ride in a car? Why or why not?

_____

_____

_____

## IV. Why?

Chemistry is the study of physical things and the matter things are made of. Chemists are scientists who do experiments to find out what physical things are like and how they change. Sometimes when matter is heated or when different kinds of matter are mixed together, a chemical process will make a change take place. By doing experiments, chemists can discover useful changes that happen to physical things. For example, chemists discovered which things when mixed together will make a soap that will take stains out of clothes.

Many daily activities use chemistry. Toothpaste is made of chemicals that help keep your teeth clean and your gums healthy. Cooking changes the chemistry of food. Eggs solidify with heat because of chemistry. Your body uses chemistry to digest the food you eat. A car is powered by the chemistry of gasoline. Painting a picture involves making mixtures and using chemicals that give off particular colors. All of these activities use chemistry.

## V. Just For Fun

Use watercolor paints for this part of the experiment.

❶ Mix blue and red together. What color do you get?

_____

❷ Mix blue and yellow together. What color do you get?

_____

❸ Mix yellow and red together. What color do you get?

_____

❹ How many colors do you need to mix together to make black?

_____

❺ Experiment with mixing the paint in different color combinations and see how many colors you can make.

❻ When the paint is dry, cut out some examples of your mixtures and tape them on the next page.

## Paint Mixtures

# Experiment 2

## The Clay Crucible

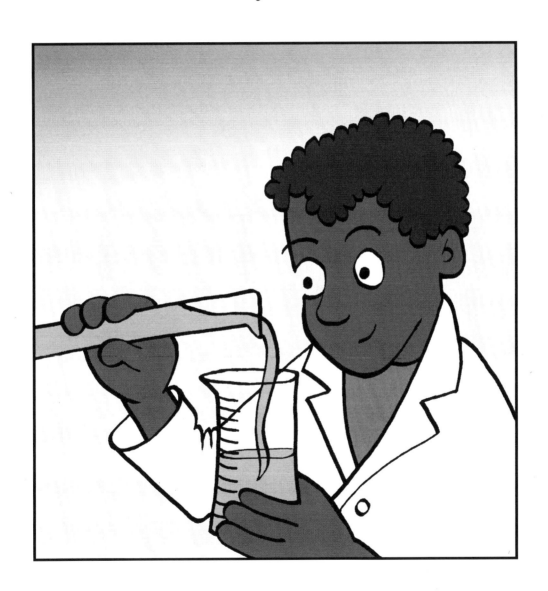

## Introduction

One common technique used by chemists for studying liquids is called *evaporation*. Some liquids are made up of different kinds molecules mixed together. One way chemists use to separate the different molecules is to use evaporation. During evaporation, some of the liquid is turned into a gas and goes into the air. This leaves behind the kinds of molecules that form a solid that can then be studied.

Chemists use a specialized tool called a *crucible* to do experiments involving evaporation. In this experiment you will explore the use of a crucible that you make.

## I. Think About It

Imagine that you have a glass of saltwater. If you mix the salt into the water and the salt is completely dissolved in the water, you won't be able to see the salt. How would you separate the salt from the water? Imagine some ways you might do this.

Draw your ideas on the next page.

## Separating Salt from Water

## II. Observe It

Take a brick of clay and mold it into a dish that will hold water. This dish is your crucible. Mix 15 ml (1 Tbsp.) of salt into 237 ml (1 cup) water. Pour some of the saltwater into the crucible and set it outside in the sunshine or in a warm place. Observe the crucible until the water is gone. Record how many hours or days it takes for all the water to disappear. Observe what is left behind. Draw or write your observations in the following chart.

| | |
|---|---|
| Date _____ <br> Time _____ | |
| Date _____ <br> Time _____ | |
| Date _____ <br> Time _____ | |
| Date _____ <br> Time _____ | |
| Date _____ <br> Time _____ | |
| Date _____ <br> Time _____ | |

## III. What Did You Discover?

**❶** How well did your crucible hold the saltwater?

_____

_____

_____

**❷** How long did it take for the water to evaporate?

_____

_____

_____

**❸** What was left behind in the crucible?

_____

_____

_____

**❹** Do you think you could modify your crucible to make it work better? Why or why not?

_____

_____

_____

_____

_____

_____

## IV. Why?

A crucible is a basic tool found in many chemistry labs. Most crucibles are made of glass or ceramic. The job of a crucible is to hold a liquid mixture and then allow the liquid to evaporate, separating it from the other things in the mixture. In this case you had a mixture of salt and water. When you poured the saltwater into the crucible and allowed the water to evaporate, only the salt was left behind.

## V. Just For Fun

Repeat the experiment with a mixture of sugar and water. Or use a mixture of sugar, salt, and water. Does the experiment still work? Does something different happen?

First, write or draw what you think will happen.

**Mixture of** _____

Now try the experiment. Follow the directions in the *Observe It* section using your new mixture.

| | |
|---|---|
| Date _____<br>Time _____ | |
| Date _____<br>Time _____ | |
| Date _____<br>Time _____ | |
| Date _____<br>Time _____ | |
| Date _____<br>Time _____ | |
| Date _____<br>Time _____ | |
| Date _____<br>Time _____ | |

# Experiment 3

# What Is It Made Of?

## I. Think About It

Write down the name of an object. Using words and drawings, describe any features you think it has.

_____   _____   _____   _____

_____   _____   _____   _____

_____   _____   _____   _____

## II. Observe It

Write down the name of the object you thought about. Describe what you actually see, using words and drawings.

## I. Think About It

Write down the name of an object. Using words and drawings, describe any features you think it has.

_____     _____     _____     _____

_____     _____     _____     _____

_____     _____     _____     _____

## II. Observe It

Write down the name of the object you thought about. Describe what you actually see, using words and drawings.

_____  _____  _____  _____
_____  _____  _____  _____
_____  _____  _____  _____

## I. Think About It

Write down the name of an object. Using words and drawings, describe any features you think it has.

## II. Observe It

Write down the name of the object you thought about. Describe what you actually see, using words and drawings.

_____     _____     _____     _____

_____     _____     _____     _____

_____     _____     _____     _____

## I. Think About It

Write down the name of an object. Using words and drawings, describe any features you think it has.

_____  _____  _____  _____
_____  _____  _____  _____
_____  _____  _____  _____

## II. Observe It

Write down the name of the object you thought about. Describe what you actually see, using words and drawings.

_____   _____   _____   _____

_____   _____   _____   _____

_____   _____   _____   _____

## I. Think About It

Write down the name of an object. Using words and drawings, describe any features you think it has.

## II. Observe It

Write down the name of the object you thought about. Describe what you actually see, using words and drawings.

_____   _____   _____   _____
_____   _____   _____   _____
_____   _____   _____   _____

## III. What Did You Discover?

❶ Were the objects you looked at the same as you expected them to be or were they different?

_____

_____

❷ How were they the same as you expected?

_____

_____

❸ How were they different from what you expected?

_____

_____

❹ Did you expect the objects to be the same on the inside and the outside or to be different?

_____

_____

❺ Which ones were the same on the inside and the outside?

_____

_____

❻ Which ones were different on the inside and the outside?

_____

_____

## IV. Why?

When we look at things around us, we often don't notice the small details. In fact, some things are too small to see with our eyes. Atoms, for example, are too small to see with our eyes, but by doing experiments scientists have discovered that everything is made of atoms.

When we take the time to look for small details, we often find amazing things we have never seen before. For example, we notice that some of the things we see are similar to each other. Different kinds of crackers, for instance, have some things that are the same as each other. Many crackers are square or round and the crackers in one box are often the same shape.

However, we also notice that even though two things may seem the same, they are not exactly the same. No two round crackers are exactly the same, and no two square crackers are exactly the same. Each one is unique. We can see the ways in which things are unique when we look at the little details.

The same is true of you. You may look similar to your mom or dad, sister or brother, but you are not exactly the same. You, too, are unique.

## V. Just For Fun

Think of a family member or friend. What things can you observe that are similar about you and the other person? What things are different?

List or draw things that are similar.

# List or draw things that are different.

_____

_____

_____

_____

_____

_____

_____

_____

_____

_____

_____

_____

_____

_____

_____

_____

# Follow the Rules!

## I. Think About It

You are going to make "molecules" with toothpicks and marshmallows. First, think about what you might find out.

❶ If you could use as many toothpicks and as many marshmallows as you wanted to, how many different shapes do you think you could make?

_____

❷ If you could stick only three toothpicks into a big marshmallow, how many shapes do you think you could make?

_____

❸ If you could stick only two toothpicks into a big marshmallow, how many shapes do you think you could make?

_____

❹ If you could stick only one toothpick into a big marshmallow, how many shapes do you think you could make?

_____

❺ What if you could not use any toothpicks at all? Could you make any shapes? Why or why not?

_____

_____

_____

_____

## II. Observe It

❶ Make as many different "molecules" as you can with the marshmallows and toothpicks.

How many can you make? _____

Can you draw one?

❷ This time you can put only three toothpicks into a big marshmallow. Following this rule, make as many different molecules as you can. A small marshmallow will go on the other end of each toothpick.

How many can you make? _____

Can you draw one?

❸ Now you can put only two toothpicks into a big marshmallow. Following this rule, make as many different molecules as you can. A small marshmallow will go on the other end of each toothpick.

How many can you make? _____

Can you draw one?

❹ Now you can put only one toothpick into a big marshmallow. Following this rule, make as many different molecules as you can. A small marshmallow will go on the other end of the toothpick.

How many can you make? _____

Can you draw one?

❺ Compare the molecules you made when you had rules to follow with the molecules you made when you did not have rules to follow.

Which ones are the same?

Can you draw two that are the same?

❻ Again compare the molecules you made when you had rules to follow with the molecules you made when you did not have rules to follow.

Which ones are different?

Can you draw two that are different?

## III. What Did You Discover?

❶ How many molecules could you make without using any rules?

_____

❷ How many molecules could you make with the rules?

_____

❸ When using the rules, could you make more molecules or fewer molecules than without the rules?

_____

❹ Why could you make more (or fewer)?

_____

_____

_____

_____

_____

_____

_____

## IV. Why?

Atoms cannot make molecules any way they want to. When atoms come together to make molecules, they must follow rules. Because they follow rules, only a certain number of molecules can be formed.

Why do you think there are rules that atoms follow when making molecules? What do you think would happen if atoms could form any kind of molecule?

Why do you have to follow rules? What do you think would happen if you could do anything you wanted to? What do you think would happen if anyone could do anything they wanted to and there were no rules at all?

Think for a moment what kind of world it might be without any rules. Chances are it would be a very difficult world to live in. Rules bring order to our lives. For the same reason, rules are important when molecules are being formed—they bring order to the process. Rules help make all of the things in the world "ordered."

## V. Just For Fun

Think of a game that you like to play and list all the rules you can think of for that game. Why are these rules important when you play the game?

OR

Make up your own game and make up the rules that would be needed to play it. What name would you give your new game?

**Game's Name** _____

**Rules** _____

_____

_____

_____

_____

_____

_____

_____

_____

_____

_____

_____

# What Will Happen?

## I. Think About It

Look at all of the things on the table. Describe them.

What do they smell like?

**A** _____

**B** _____

**C** _____

**D** _____

What color are they?

**A** _____

**B** _____

**C** _____

**D** _____

Are they thick or thin?

**A** _____

**B** _____

**C** _____

**D** _____

## II. Observe It

❶ What will happen if you add **A** to **B**?
Can you guess?

_____

_____

Now, add **A** to **B**.
What happened?
Describe what happened and draw a picture.

_____

_____

_____

❷ What will happen if you add **A** to **C**?
Can you guess?

_____

_____

Now, add **A** to **C**.
What happened?
Describe what happened and draw a picture.

_____

_____

_____

_____

❸ What will happen if you add **A** to **D**?
Can you guess?

_____

_____

Now, add **A** to **D**.
What happened?
Describe what happened and draw a picture.

_____

_____

_____

_____

_____

❹ What will happen if you add **B** to **C**?
Can you guess?

_____

_____

Now, add **B** to **C**.
What happened?
Describe what happened and draw a picture.

_____

_____

_____

_____

❺ **What will happen if you add B to D?**
   **Can you guess?**

_____

_____

**Now, add B to D.**
**What happened?**
**Describe what happened and draw a picture.**

_____

_____

_____

_____

**❻** What will happen if you add **C** to **D**?
Can you guess?

_____

_____

Now, add **C** to **D**.
What happened?
Describe what happened and draw a picture.

_____

_____

_____

_____

## Summary

Summarize your answers.

❶ Did lemon juice (**A**) react with vinegar (**B**)? _____

❷ Did lemon juice (**A**) react with milk (**C**)? _____

❸ Did lemon juice (**A**) react with baking soda (**D**)? _____

❹ Did vinegar (**B**) react with milk (**C**)? _____

❺ Did vinegar (**B**) react with baking soda (**D**)? _____

❻ Did milk (**C**) react with baking soda (**D**)? _____

❼ What things did you notice that told you whether a reaction took place or did not take place?

_____

_____

_____

_____

_____

## III. What Did You Discover?

❶ What happened when you added **A** to **B**?

_____

❷ What happened when you added **A** to **D**?

_____

❸ Were they different? If so, how?

_____

❹ Were some of the reactions the same? Which ones?

_____

❺ Could you guess what would happen before you added them together?

_____

❻ Did you guess correctly?

_____

❼ Why or why not?

_____

_____

_____

_____

## IV. Why?

Why did some of the liquids you mixed react and some did not? It turns out that not every molecule will react with every other molecule. Molecules follow "rules" when they react, just like atoms follow rules to make molecules. The rules tell the molecules which molecules they can react with and which molecules they can't react with.

Vinegar and lemon juice both react with milk. Vinegar and lemon juice also both react with baking soda. Vinegar and lemon juice are similar to each other. That is why they react in similar ways.

Although both vinegar and lemon juice reacted with milk and baking soda, the reactions were different. When added to milk, the vinegar and the lemon juice each made the milk curdle. When added to baking soda, the vinegar and the lemon juice each made bubbles. Milk and baking soda do not have the same type of molecules in them, so they had different types of chemical reactions with the vinegar and the lemon juice. The molecules combined in different ways.

## V. Just For Fun

Try another mixing experiment to see what will happen.

Put some baking soda in a cup. Add some sugar. Now pour in some vinegar. What happens? Is it different from what happened when you mixed just baking soda and vinegar without the sugar? On the next page, write or draw what you observe.

If you like, you can repeat this experiment, using differing amounts of baking soda, sugar, and vinegar. Observe whether this makes a difference in the reaction.

Or, find two food items in your kitchen that you haven't already used in a mixture. What do you think might happen when you mix them together? Now mix them. What actually happens? Write or draw what you observe. You can repeat this experiment by mixing the two items in different amounts, or you can try mixing other combinations of two food items.

## Experiment 6

# Sour or Not Sour?

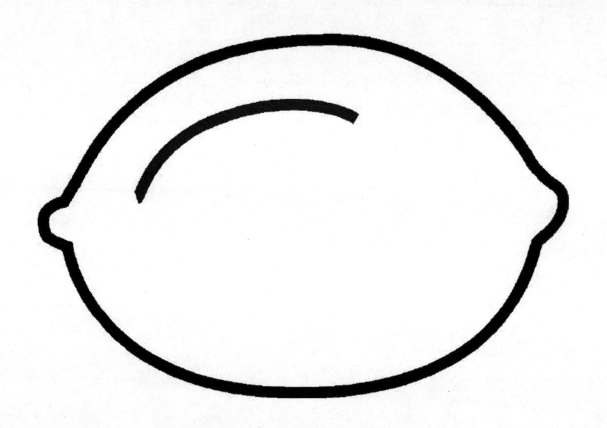

## I. Think About It

Think about each of the liquids listed in the chart below and whether it would taste "sour" or "not sour." Use a check mark to record your answer.

| Liquid | Sour | Not Sour |
|---|---|---|
| white grape juice | | |
| milk | | |
| lemon juice | | |
| grapefruit juice | | |
| mineral water | | |
| antacid | | |
| distilled water | | |
| baking soda water | | |

## II. Observe It

❶ Tear out the following pages labeled "SOUR" and "NOT SOUR," and place them on a table. Next, taste the liquids and record which are sour and which are not sour. After you test each liquid, place the cup on the paper that has the label that matches the taste.

| Liquid | Sour | Not Sour |
|---|---|---|
| white grape juice | | |
| milk | | |
| lemon juice | | |
| grapefruit juice | | |
| mineral water | | |
| antacid | | |
| distilled water | | |
| baking soda water | | |

# SOUR

# NOT SOUR
## (sweet or salty)

❷ Next, pour 60 milliliters (1/4 cup) of red cabbage juice into a plastic cup that contains a liquid you tasted.

❸ Observe what happens. Does the red cabbage juice change color? Record your observations below.

❹ Repeat Steps ❷-❸ for each of the liquids you tasted.

| Liquid | Color change? (yes or no) | What is the color? |
|---|---|---|
| white grape juice | | |
| milk | | |
| lemon juice | | |
| grapefruit juice | | |
| mineral water | | |
| antacid | | |
| distilled water | | |
| baking soda water | | |

## III. What Did You Discover?

❶ Which liquids were sour?

_____

_____

❷ Which liquids were not sour?

_____

_____

❸ When you added the cabbage juice to the "sour" liquids, what color did the cabbage juice become?

_____

_____

❹ When you added the cabbage juice to the "not sour" liquids, what color did the cabbage juice become?

_____

_____

❺ Why do you think the "sour" liquids and "not sour" liquids turned the cabbage juice different colors?

_____

_____

❻ If you added cabbage juice to a drink and it turned pink, do you think that drink would taste sour?

_____

_____

## IV. Why?

You may have observed that the liquids that were very sour, or even a little bit sour, turned the cabbage juice pink when it was added. You may also have noticed that the liquids that were not sour, and maybe tasted bitter or salty, turned the cabbage juice green when it was added. You may have noticed that milk and water didn't change the color of the cabbage juice, but instead the cabbage juice turned the milk and water purple. Do you know why?

The red cabbage juice is called an *indicator*. In chemistry an indicator is something that tests a substance. In this case, the red cabbage juice is an indicator that tests whether a liquid is an acid or a base. The sour liquids are acids, and the bitter or salty liquids are bases. Milk and water don't change the color of the red cabbage juice indicator at all, so they are neither acids nor bases. They are called neutral.

An acid will always change the color of the red cabbage juice indicator to pink, and a base will always change the color of the red cabbage juice indicator to green. A neutral liquid, like milk or water, will never change the color of the red cabbage juice indicator.

This is why the liquids turned pink, green, or purple when the red cabbage juice was added!

## V. Just For Fun

Look around for some other liquids you can test with the red cabbage juice indicator. Observe whether the cabbage juice changes color when added to the liquids.

**Do not taste** these liquids, but decide if each is an acid, a base, or neutral according to the color change. Record your observations.

| LIQUID | ACID, BASE, OR NEUTRAL |
|--------|------------------------|
|        |                        |
|        |                        |
|        |                        |
|        |                        |
|        |                        |
|        |                        |
|        |                        |
|        |                        |
|        |                        |
|        |                        |

## Experiment 7

# Pink and Green Together

## Introduction

In the last experiment we added red cabbage juice indicator to different liquids and they changed color. Some turned pink, some turned green, and some turned purple. We found that the pink liquids were acids, the green liquids were bases, and the purple liquids were neither acids nor bases but were neutral.

## I. Think About It

❶ What do you think will happen if you add a pink liquid to a green liquid?

_____

_____

❷ Do you think the color will change or stay the same? Why?

_____

_____

❸ Do you think a pink liquid will turn green if a green liquid is added? Why?

_____

_____

❹ Do you think a green liquid will turn pink if a pink liquid is added? Why?

_____

_____

❺ Do you think they will turn orange, blue, or even black? Why?

_____

_____

## II. Observe It

❶ Take the red cabbage juice, add it to the following liquids, and then record the color.

| Liquid | Pink | Green | Purple |
|---|---|---|---|
| distilled water | | | |
| mineral water | | | |
| lemon juice | | | |
| vinegar | | | |
| baking soda water | | | |
| antacid water | | | |

❷ Mix the pink liquids and the green liquids together and observe whether or not they change color. Record your observations.

| | antacid water | lemon juice | vinegar | mineral water | distilled water | baking soda water |
|---|---|---|---|---|---|---|
| **antacid water** | | | | | | |
| **lemon juice** | | | | | | |
| **vinegar** | | | | | | |
| **mineral water** | | | | | | |
| **distilled water** | | | | | | |
| **baking soda water** | | | | | | |

❸ Complete the above chart by mixing the rest of the liquids together and recording the results.

## III. What Did You Discover?

❶ What happened when you added a pink liquid to a green liquid?

_____

_____

_____

❷ What happened when you added a green liquid to a pink liquid?

_____

_____

_____

❸ Did you get different colors when you added different liquids together?

_____

_____

_____

❹ Did any of the colors stay pink, green, or purple?

_____

_____

_____

## IV. Why?

You may have seen that when you added the pink liquids to the green liquids, the pink liquids turned green. You may also have noticed that when you added the pink liquids to the green liquids, the green liquids turned pink. You may have observed that when you kept adding the liquids together, all of the liquids turned purple (the same color that water turns with the cabbage juice indicator). Why? Why do the pink or green liquids change color, and why do all of the liquids turn purple at the end?

Remember that the pink liquids are acids, and the green liquids are bases. When acids and bases are added together, they react. That is, they change—the acids lose what makes them acids, and the bases lose what makes them bases.

This is why all of the liquids turn purple when you continue to mix them. They turn into a liquid that is neither an acid nor a base—it is neutral, like water!

## V. Just For Fun

Find different liquids to mix together and test with the red cabbage juice indicator. You might try mixing soda pop with baking soda water and white grape juice with baking soda water. What happens if you mix the mixtures together? What other mixtures can you make and then mix together? Record your observations.

### Mixture Observations

# Experiment 8

## Make It Mix!

## Introduction

What happens when different liquids are mixed together? Try this experiment to find out.

## I. Think About It

Look at each item in the first row of the chart below. If you think the item is "like oil," put a check mark in the row labeled "Like Oil." If you think it is "like water," put a check mark in the row labeled "Like Water."

|  | Water | Milk | Juice | Oil | Butter |
|---|---|---|---|---|---|
| **Like Oil** |  |  |  |  |  |
| **Like Water** |  |  |  |  |  |

❶ What do you think will happen if you add water to milk?

_____

_____

_____

_____

❷ What do you think will happen if you add milk to juice?

_____

_____

_____

_____

❸ What do you think will happen if you add juice to oil?

_____

_____

_____

_____

❹ What do you think will happen if you add oil to water?

_____

_____

_____

_____

❺ What do you think will happen if you add oil to melted butter?

_____

_____

_____

_____

❻ What do you think will happen if you add soap to water and then add oil?

_____

_____

_____

_____

## II. Observe It

Mix two liquids together and record below whether they mix or don't mix. Use about 15 ml (1 Tbsp.) of each liquid when making the mixtures and use a separate cup for each mixture. Label each cup with the contents.

### Results of Mixing Liquids

| | Water | Milk | Juice | Oil | Butter |
|---|---|---|---|---|---|
| **Water** | | | | | |
| **Milk** | | | | | |
| **Juice** | | | | | |
| **Oil** | | | | | |
| **Butter** | | | | | |

## Observe It With Soap

Take your mixtures from the first part of the experiment and add soap to each mixture. Note whether the addition of soap changes the way the liquids mix. Record your observations in the chart below.

### Results of Adding Soap to Mixtures

|         | Water | Milk | Juice | Oil | Butter |
|---------|-------|------|-------|-----|--------|
| Water   |       |      |       |     |        |
| Milk    |       |      |       |     |        |
| Juice   |       |      |       |     |        |
| Oil     |       |      |       |     |        |
| Butter  |       |      |       |     |        |

## III. What Did You Discover?

❶ What happened when you added milk to juice? Did they mix? Was this what you expected?

_____

_____

❷ What happened when you added water to juice? Did they mix? Was this what you expected?

_____

_____

❸ What happened when you added oil to water? Did they mix? Was this what you expected?

_____

_____

❹ What happened when you added soap to your mixtures? Did the soap, water, and juice mix better?

_____

_____

❺ Did the water and oil mix better with soap?

_____

❻ Did the oil and butter mix better with soap?

_____

## IV. Why?

When you added milk to juice, or water to milk, you should have seen that they mix. *Mixing* is when two things blend together so well that you can no longer tell them apart. Milk is white and juice is colored. When they are added together, the mixture of the two is a new color, a cloudy color. Juice and milk, water and milk, and juice and water mix because they all are the same type of liquid.

What happens when you add oil to water, or oil to juice? Do they mix? You should have seen that when you added oil to water or oil to juice, they did not mix. No matter how much you try to get oil and water or oil and juice to mix, you will always be able to see little droplets of oil floating around, not mixing. Oil and water cannot be mixed because they are *different* types of liquids.

You should have seen that when you added oil to butter, the two mixed. Why do you think this happened? It happened because oil and melted butter are the *same* type of liquids.

The rule is: *Liquids of the same type mix and liquids of different types do not mix.*

What happens with soap? Soap is a little bit like water and a little bit like oil, so soap can make water and oil "mix" a little bit. This is why you use soap to wash oils off your hands!

## V. Just For Fun

Think about different ways you might test liquids to find out whether they are "like water" or "like oil." Use one of your ideas to create an experiment to find out if the following liquids are "like water" or "like oil."

→ Soda

→ Coconut oil (or olive oil, canola oil, or other vegetable oil)

→ Orange juice

→ Mayonnaise

→ Another liquid of your choice

Record your observations in the chart on the next page, or make up your own chart. Name your experiment and write the name on the chart. Below the chart make notes about how you performed this experiment. Also record whether or not you think the experiment worked and why or why not.

|  |  |  |  |  |  |
|---|---|---|---|---|---|
|  |  |  |  |  |  |
|  |  |  |  |  |  |
|  |  |  |  |  |  |
|  |  |  |  |  |  |
|  |  |  |  |  |  |

_____

_____

_____

_____

_____

_____

# Experiment 9

## Make It Un-mix!

## Introduction

Do this experiment to discover some ways to separate different kinds of mixtures.

## I. Think About It

**❶** If you had rocks and Legos mixed together, how would you un-mix them?

_____

_____

**❷** If you had rocks and sand in a bag, how would you un-mix them?

_____

_____

**❸** If you had sand and salt in a bag, how would you un-mix them?

_____

_____

**❹** If you had salt and sugar in a bag, how would you un-mix them?

_____

_____

**❺** If you had salt and sugar in water, how would you un-mix them?

_____

_____

## II. Observe It

❶ Take a handful of rocks and a handful of Legos and mix
them together on the table. Now try to un-mix them. Draw
or describe what you did.

_____

_____

_____

_____

_____

_____

❷ Take a handful of rocks and mix them with sand in a bag. Now un-mix the rocks and sand. Draw or describe what you did.

_____

_____

_____

_____

_____

_____

_____

❸ Take a handful of sand and a handful of salt and mix them in
a bag. Now un-mix them. Draw or describe what you did.

_____

_____

_____

_____

_____

_____

_____

❹ Place a few drops of several different colors of food coloring into a glass or paper cup that contains 120 ml (1/2 cup) of water. Think about ways you might un-mix the colors.

❺ Now try a method called *chromatography* which uses paper to un-mix the colors.

Take a piece of coffee filter paper and cut it into long strips. Place a pencil over the top of the glass or paper cup that contains the colored water mixture and tape one end of a paper strip to the middle of the pencil. The other end of the filter paper will be in the colored water.

It should look like this:

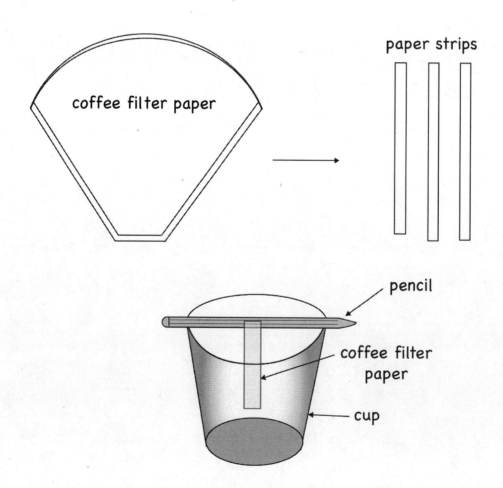

coffee filter paper

paper strips

pencil

coffee filter paper

cup

**❻** Carefully observe what happens, and record your observations.

_____

_____

_____

_____

_____

_____

_____

Let the filter paper dry and tape it in the box.

❼ Repeat the experiment with an "unknown." Have someone mix two colors together in water. See if you can tell, using chromatography, which colors are in the water.

❽ Make an unknown for your teacher. Mix two colors together without telling your teacher what they are. Have your teacher use chromatography to find out which colors you put in the glass.

❾ Record all of your results below.

## Your Unknown

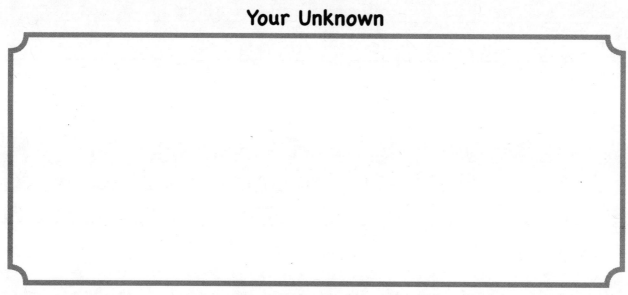

## Teacher's Unknown

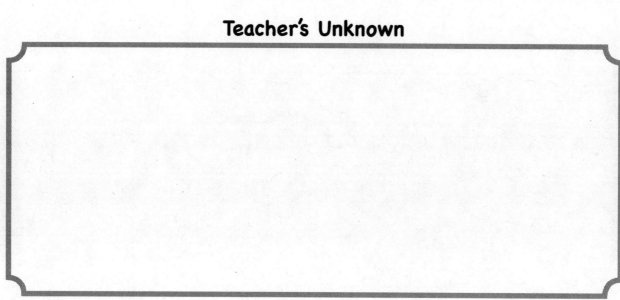

## III. What Did You Discover?

**❶** How many different ways did you discover to un-mix things that were mixed? List them.

_____     _____

_____     _____

_____     _____

_____     _____

**❷** Can you use your fingers to un-mix the rocks and Legos? Can you use water? Can you use paper? Why or why not?

_____

_____

_____

_____

**❸** Can you use your fingers to un-mix the sand and the rocks? Can you use water? Can you use paper? Why or why not?

_____

_____

_____

_____

❹ Can you use your fingers to un-mix the sand and the salt?
Can you use water? Can you use paper? Why or why not?

_____

_____

_____

_____

_____

❺ Can you use your fingers to un-mix the colors in the water?
Can you use water? Can you use paper? Why or why not?

_____

_____

_____

_____

_____

## IV. Why?

You found out in the last experiment that some items mix and some do not. In this experiment you discovered that sometimes you can un-mix items and sometimes you cannot. You also discovered that large objects, like rocks and Legos, are easier to un-mix than small items, like salt and sand. You discovered that items that look similar, like salt and sugar, are difficult to un-mix.

Why are some mixtures hard to separate and some easy? Larger objects, like rocks and Legos, are easier to un-mix than smaller items like sand and salt. Items that have very different properties, like sand and sugar, are easier to separate than items that are very similar, like salt and sugar. Also, very small objects that are hard to see are very difficult to separate. For example, molecules are very difficult to separate from other molecules.

You found out that when items are difficult to un-mix you can use a few "tricks," one of which is *chromatography.*

## V. Just For Fun

Take a handful of salt and a handful of sugar and mix them in a bag. Now un-mix them. Draw or describe what you did.

_____

_____

_____

_____

_____

_____

_____

# Experiment 10

# Making Goo

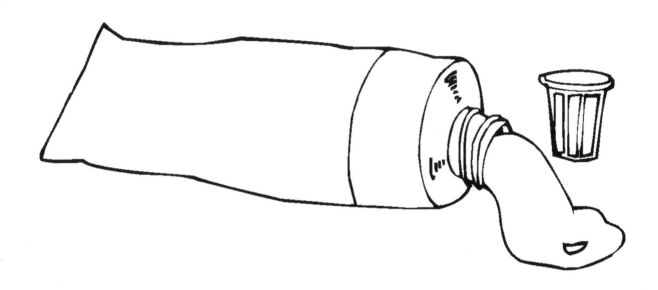

## Introduction

Explore how the properties of substances can change when the substances are mixed together.

## I. Think About It

❶ How does glue feel on your fingers? Can you roll it into a ball? Why or why not?

_____

_____

_____

❷ How does laundry starch feel on your fingers?

_____

_____

_____

❸ What do you think would happen if you added laundry starch to the glue?

_____

_____

_____

❹ Do you think the glue would feel the same as it did before you added laundry starch to it? Why or why not?

_____

_____

_____

❺ What do you think would happen if you added glue to the laundry starch?

_____

_____

_____

❻ Do you think the laundry starch would feel the same as it did before you added glue to it? Why or why not?

_____

_____

_____

## II. Observe It

❶ Take a small plastic cup and put about 30-60 ml (1/8-1/4 cup) of white Elmer's glue in it.

❷ Now add 30-60 ml (1/8-1/4 cup) of liquid laundry starch to the Elmer's glue.

❸ Mix the glue and starch with your fingers.

❹ Pay careful attention to any changes that occur. Think about how the glue might be changing or how the starch might be changing.

❺ Try to roll the glue and laundry starch into a ball. Are you able to do it?

_____

_____

## III. What Did You Discover?

❶ What happened when you mixed the starch and glue together?

_____

_____

_____

❷ Could you feel the glue and/or starch change?

_____

_____

_____

❸ What did it feel like? Could you roll the mixture into a ball?

_____

_____

_____

❹ Do you think this means there was a *chemical reaction?*

_____

_____

_____

## IV. Why?

You discovered that when you mixed glue and starch together, something happened. The glue became less sticky, and you found you could easily roll it into a ball.

When glue and laundry starch are added to each other, a *chemical reaction* occurs. You can see that a reaction has occurred because the glue and the laundry starch are different than they were before you mixed them together. The glue loses its stickiness and can be easily rolled into a ball.

The reaction you observed occurs between the molecules in the glue and the molecules in the laundry starch. Glue is made of long chains of molecules called *polymers*. The laundry starch hooks these polymers together by means of a chemical reaction. The reaction changes the way the polymers move around, and this changes the properties of the glue and the starch.

## V. Just For Fun

Repeat the experiment using a different glue to see if it makes a difference in the results. Some ideas for glues are: blue glue, clear glue, wood glue, glitter glue, or paste glue. You can also try adding a little food coloring to your mixture.

In the box below, record your observations.

# Experiment 11

## Salty or Sweet?

## Introduction

The tongue is an amazing indicator. In this experiment you will explore the tastes of different foods.

## I. Think About It

**❶ How do marshmallows taste? Are they salty, sweet, or neither?**

_____

**❷ How do pretzels taste? Are they salty, sweet, or neither?**

_____

**❸ How do ripe bananas taste? Are they salty, sweet, or neither?**

_____

**❹ How do green bananas taste? Are they salty, sweet, or neither?**

_____

**❺ How do raw potatoes taste? Are they salty, sweet, or neither?**

_____

**❻ How do cooked potatoes taste? Are they salty, sweet, or neither?**

_____

## II. Observe It

Tear out the pages that say **SALTY**, **SWEET**, and **NEITHER**, and place them on a table.

Take a number of different food items and spread them out on the table. Guess whether each food item is salty, sweet, or neither. Place each food item on the labeled page that matches your guess.

Now have your teacher place a blindfold over your eyes. Taste each food item and see if you can tell if it is salty, sweet, or neither.

# SALTY

# SWEET

# NEITHER

## III. What Did You Discover?

**❶** How many foods did you find that were sweet?

_____

**❷** How many foods did you find that were salty?

_____

**❸** How many foods did you find that were neither salty nor sweet?

_____

**❹** Did any of your results surprise you? What were they?

_____

_____

_____

_____

_____

_____

_____

**❺** How many food tastes did you guess correctly?

_____

**❻** How many food tastes did you guess incorrectly?

_____

## IV. Why?

Why were some of the foods you tasted salty, some sweet, and some neither?

The reason foods taste salty or sweet has to do with the different molecules that are in the food. Fruit, candy, soda pop, and even yams have sugar in them. The taste buds on your tongue tell your brain that these foods have sugar in them. Potato chips, pretzels, and anchovies have salt in them. Your taste buds tell your brain that these foods contain salt.

Your taste buds are designed to tell the difference between foods that are salty and those that are sweet. Taste buds can also tell the difference between foods that are sour and ones that are bitter. Taste buds are pretty amazing!

Some foods contain long chains of sugar molecules, called *carbohydrates*. Potatoes and green bananas contain carbohydrates. Your taste buds can't tell that these long chains of molecules are made of sugar, so these foods don't taste sweet. When the long chains of sugar molecules (carbohydrates) are broken apart, your taste buds can detect the sugar and then the food tastes sweet. Ripe bananas are sweeter than green bananas and cooked potatoes are sweeter than raw potatoes because their long chains of sugar molecules have been broken apart.

## V. Just For Fun

Everyone is different. Not everyone tastes food the same way you do. Repeat the experiment with your mom or dad, a sister or brother, or a neighbor. See if you get the same results. Record your observations.

**How Does It Taste?**

# Experiment 12

## Make It Rise!

## Introduction

Discover more about molecules in food and the body.

## I. Think About It

❶ List as many different types of molecules as you can.

_____

_____

_____

_____

_____

❷ What kinds of molecules make food salty?

_____

❸ What kinds of molecules are glue and starch made of?

_____

❹ Do you think all the molecules in your body would work properly if your body got too hot? Why or why not?

_____

_____

❺ What kinds of molecules do you think make bread rise?

_____

_____

## II. Observe It

**❶** Open one package of active dry yeast. In a bowl, dissolve 1/2 of the yeast in 240 ml (1 cup) of lukewarm water. Label this **Dough A**. In a second bowl, dissolve the remaining half of the yeast in 240 ml (1 cup) of cold water and label it **Dough B**.

**❷** Add 15 ml (1 Tbsp.) of sugar and 15 ml (1 Tbsp.) of oil to each bowl and mix.

**❸** Add 475 ml (2 cups) of flour to each yeast mixture. Mix and knead.

**❹** Coat two bowls with oil. Place **Dough A** in one bowl and **Dough B** in the other bowl. Put the bowl with **Dough A** in a warm, moist place, and put the bowl with **Dough B** in the refrigerator.

**❺** Let the doughs rise for one to one and a half hours.

**❻** After the doughs have risen, carefully observe any differences.

**❼** Punch down each dough. Return **Dough B** to the refrigerator and let the doughs rise again for another hour.

**❽** Shape the doughs into loaves and bake at 190°C (375°F) for 35-40 minutes.

## III. What Did You Discover?

**❶** Describe what happened to the dough that was made with warm water and put in a warm place.

_____

_____

_____

**❷** Describe what happened to the dough that was made with cold water and placed in the refrigerator.

_____

_____

_____

**❸** Was there a difference between the two doughs?

_____

_____

_____

**❹** What was different about how you made the two doughs? Do you think this difference might have made the doughs behave differently?

_____

_____

_____

## IV. Why?

You should have discovered that the dough made with cold water and placed in the refrigerator did not rise. The dough made with warm water and placed in a warm place did rise. The dough made with cold water and placed in the refrigerator did not rise because yeast is made of living cells and living cells often need warm temperatures to live.

Yeast has molecules in it called *enzymes*. Enzymes produce the molecules that make bread rise. Many enzymes need warm temperatures in order to work properly. In fact, inside your body there are many enzymes that do a variety of jobs. Some enzymes cut molecules, some read other molecules, some copy other molecules, and some glue molecules together. All of the enzymes in your body work at your body temperature. If your body gets too hot or too cold, your enzymes can't work—just like the yeast enzymes could not make the molecules needed for dough to rise when it was made with cold water and placed in the refrigerator.

## V. Just For Fun

### Baking Powder (or Not) Biscuits

For this experiment see what happens when you make biscuits with and without baking powder. Before starting the experiment, record what you think will happen. Space is provided on the following page.

❶ Take two mixing bowls and label one **Dough A** and the other **Dough B**.

❷ Into each bowl measure 475 ml (2 cups) flour and 2.5 ml (1/2 teaspoon) salt. Mix together.

❸ Add 15 ml (1 Tbsp.) of baking powder to **Dough A only**.

❹ To each bowl add 60 ml (1/4 cup) soft butter. Mix with your fingers until the butter is well mixed in. The dough should look something like cornmeal.

❺ To each bowl add 180 ml (3/4 cup) milk and mix until the dough particles cling together.

❻ Knead each dough on a floured board for about 1 minute.

❼ Take biscuit size pieces of dough and pat them into biscuits that are about 2 cm (3/4 inch) thick. Or roll out the dough to the same thickness and use a biscuit cutter.

❽ Place each biscuit on an ungreased cookie sheet. Use a separate cookie sheet for each dough mixture.

❾ Bake at 232°C (450°F) for 12–15 minutes until golden.

❿ Record your observations of **Dough A** and **Dough B**.

# Baking Powder (or Not) Biscuits

## Thoughts about what will happen

### Dough A

_____

_____

_____

### Dough B

_____

_____

_____

## Results of the experiment

### Dough A

_____

_____

_____

### Dough B

_____

_____

_____

# More REAL SCIENCE-4-KIDS Books
## by Rebecca W. Keller, PhD

**Building Blocks Series** yearlong study program — each Student Textbook has accompanying Laboratory Notebook, Teacher's Manual, Lesson Plan, Study Notebook, Quizzes, and Graphics Package

Exploring Science Book K (Activity Book)
Exploring Science Book 1
Exploring Science Book 2
Exploring Science Book 3
Exploring Science Book 4
Exploring Science Book 5
Exploring Science Book 6
Exploring Science Book 7
Exploring Science Book 8

**Focus On Series** unit study program — each title has a Student Textbook with accompanying Laboratory Notebook, Teacher's Manual, Lesson Plan, Study Notebook, Quizzes, and Graphics Package

Focus On Elementary Chemistry
Focus On Elementary Biology
Focus On Elementary Physics
Focus On Elementary Geology
Focus On Elementary Astronomy

Focus On Middle School Chemistry
Focus On Middle School Biology
Focus On Middle School Physics
Focus On Middle School Geology
Focus On Middle School Astronomy

Focus On High School Chemistry

## Super Simple Science Experiments

21 Super Simple Chemistry Experiments
21 Super Simple Biology Experiments
21 Super Simple Physics Experiments
21 Super Simple Geology Experiments
21 Super Simple Astronomy Experiments
101 Super Simple Science Experiments

**Note:** A few titles may still be in production.

## Gravitas Publications Inc.
www.gravitaspublications.com
www.realscience4kids.com